SLUMDOG MILLIONAIRE

A FILM BY DANNY BOYLE

LEVEL 4

SCHOLASTIC

Adapted by: Paul Shipton

Fact Files written by: Jacquie Bloese

Publisher: Jacquie Bloese

Editor: Cheryl Pelteret

Designer: Mo Choy

Picture research: Pupak Navabpour

Photo credits:
Cover: © Pathe Productions Limited
Film stills provided courtesy of Celador Films and Channel 4
Television Corporation Limited.
Stills photographer: Ishika Mohan
Page 5: F Soltan/Corbis; nagelestock/Alamy; S Crasto/
Reuters. **Page 33:** J McCauley/Rex **Page 78:** F Harrison/Getty
Images. **Pages 80 & 81:** AFP/Getty Images; M Manglani/
Reuters; Mary Evans Picture Library. **Pages 82 & 83:** P Singh,
N Nanu/AFP/Getty Images; childrenwalkingtall.com.
Page 82: Interview with Rukshana reproduced with
permission from the *New Internationalist* magazine

Published by Scholastic Ltd. 2010

Mary Glasgow Magazines (Scholastic Ltd.)
Euston House
24 Eversholt Street
London NW1 IDB

Printed in Malaysia

Reprinted in 2010, 2012, 2013, 2014, 2015, 2016, 2017, 2018, 2019 and 2020

Contents

Page

JAMAL MALIK

works as an assistant in a call centre in Mumbai. When he goes on the TV programme *Who Wants To Be A Millionaire?*, nobody expects him to win much money. But Jamal has a special reason for wanting to go on the programme ... .

LATIKA

first meets Jamal when they are both children with no parents and no home. They become close friends. Later Jamal loses Latika but his love for her never dies.

MAMAN

offers a home to children who have no parents. He seems kind but he is not; he uses the children to earn money for him by begging.

JAVED

is the most powerful crime boss in the slum where Jamal and Salim live. He is used to getting what he wants, and his violent crimes have made him a rich man.

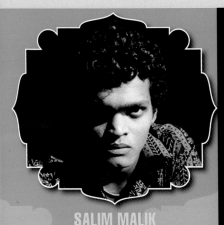

SALIM MALIK

is Jamal's older brother. After the boys' mother dies, Salim looks after Jamal. But as they grow older, things change and Salim moves towards a life of crime.

PREM KUMAR

is the television presenter who asks the questions on *Who Wants To Be A Millionaire?*. He sees himself as the star of the programme.

PLACES

MUMBAI is India's largest city, with over 14 million people. Although the city is a growing centre of business, there are many poor people. Jamal and Salim grow up in a poor area of the city, a slum called Juhu.

THE TAJ MAHAL, in Agra, is one of the world's most famous buildings and tourist attractions. It was built by an Indian ruler in the 17th century in memory of his dead wife.

THE CALL CENTRE is the place where Jamal works. Here, hundreds of workers make sales calls to customers in Britain.

SLUMDOG MILLIONAIRE

PROLOGUE

In the biggest quiz programme on Indian television, Jamal Malik is one question away from winning 20 million rupees*. How did he do it?

◆A: He cheated.

◆B: He's lucky.

◆C: He's brilliant.

◆D: It is his destiny.

✳ ✳ ✳

The prisoner's hands were tied together and he was hanging from the ceiling. Exhausted, Jamal just wanted to close his eyes, but he was in so much pain that sleep was impossible.

The Inspector walked into the room and looked over at Jamal. 'Has he told the truth yet?' he asked.

Constable† Srinivas jumped to his feet. 'He's told me his name,' he explained. 'Nothing else.'

'But you've been here with him the whole night!' the Inspector shouted. 'What have you been doing?'

'He's a tough guy,' Srinivas said, looking at the young prisoner.

The Inspector thought for a moment. 'Maybe a little electricity will help him talk.'

---

* Rupees are the money used in India. 20 million rupees is a huge amount of money.

† A police officer.

While Srinivas fetched a box from a cupboard in the room and began to attach it to Jamal's feet and chest, the Inspector bent down to speak to Jamal.

'It's a hot day,' he said, 'and Mumbai is full of murderers, robbers, thieves ... and you. So why not save us both a lot of time? Tell me how you cheated.'

Jamal continued to stare silently into the Inspector's eyes. The Inspector gave the order and Constable Srinivas turned the machine on. Electricity ran through Jamal's body. It was impossible not to cry out. The machine was only on for a few seconds, but the pain that ran through Jamal's body filled his whole world.

The Inspector walked up to him again, ready to ask more questions. Then he noticed the problem ... .

'He's unconscious!' he cried angrily. 'How many times have I told you ... ?'

'Sorry, sir,' said Srinivas.

'Just get him down and tidy him up,' said the Inspector.

Srinivas didn't move. Something was troubling him, but he was almost too afraid to say it. 'Sir, maybe ... maybe he *did* know the answers?'

The Inspector could hardly contain his anger. 'Teachers, lawyers, doctors ... they never win more than sixteen thousand rupees. And he's won ten million rupees! He's from the slums! What can a *slumdog** know?'

A low voice came from the other side of the room. 'The answers,' said Jamal quietly. Ignoring the pain, he lifted his head. 'I knew ... the answers.'

* * *

An hour later, Jamal was sitting at the Inspector's desk. In the corner of the room there was a television and video player. Srinivas pressed PLAY and Jamal heard the music he knew so well. That music meant one thing – the start of *Who Wants To Be A Millionaire?*.

The studio audience was cheering loudly. Sitting in the Inspector's office now, Jamal couldn't believe that he had been in the television studio less than a day ago. 'Welcome to *Who Wants To Be A Millionaire?*!' Prem Kumar, the programme's presenter, was saying. 'Please welcome our first contestant of the evening ... from here in Mumbai, Jamal Malik!'

Jamal turned to the screen and watched himself walking out into the bright lights of the television studio ... .

* An impolite description of a person who lives in the slums.

CHAPTER 1
The first question

Jamal had never been in a television studio before, or in front of so many people. He felt nervous in his best white shirt, as Prem Kumar led him to his seat and silenced the audience with one hand.

'So Jamal, tell me about yourself.'

'I work in a call centre.'

A thin smile appeared on Prem's face. 'So *you're* the one who calls me every day with special offers?'

As the audience began to laugh, Jamal replied, 'Actually, I'm an assistant.'

'An *assistant*?' Prem's smile grew wider. 'So what does an assistant in a call centre do exactly?'

'I ... make tea for people and ... '

'You're a *chai-wallah**?' interrupted Prem, sounding

---

* A *chai-wallah* is a person who serves tea in a building.

surprised. He looked round at the audience, laughing, and repeated, 'A *chai-wallah*!' The laughter in the studio grew louder.

Still smiling, Prem turned his attention back to the contestant opposite him. 'Well, Jamal Malik, *chai-wallah* from Mumbai ... let's play *Who Wants To Be A Millionaire?*!'

The music started again and the audience cheered.

'So Jamal, are you ready to answer the first question, for one thousand rupees?' asked Prem.

'Yes.' Jamal knew that each question was worth more money than the last. But if he gave just one incorrect answer, that would be the end of the game for him. Under the rules of the quiz, he had just three 'lifelines'* to help him: he could 'Ask The Audience'; he could use '50:50' to take away two of the possible answers; and he could 'Phone-A-Friend'.

Prem was still smiling. 'Not bad money to sit on a chair and answer a question, huh? Better than making tea. No?'

'No ... ,' said Jamal, unsure how to answer. 'Yes. No!'

'Is that your final answer?' Prem said with a smile, turning to the audience, who began to laugh again.

When silence returned to the studio, Prem's voice became more serious. It was time for the first question. As Prem read it out, the question appeared on the computer screen in front of Jamal.

Who was the star of the 1973 film *Zanjeer*?

'Was it A, Amitabh Bachchan? Was it B ... '

Prem read out the rest of the answers, but Jamal was hardly listening. A name was calling to him from the past.

---

* A way to get help with the answers in the game *Who Wants To Be A Millionaire?*.

It had been years since he had last thought about the film star, Amitabh Bachchan. Jamal had been just a boy ... .

∗ ∗ ∗

When Jamal was seven years old, he had liked nothing more than playing cricket in the sun with his older brother Salim and the other children in Juhu, a slum in Mumbai. Their mother had other ideas. Sometimes she used to drag them to school, pulling them behind her by their T-shirts.

The classroom was crowded and the teacher had to shout so that the children could hear him.

'The Three Musketeers*!' *he shouted out the title of the old story book in his hands. He began to call out the names of the characters from the book.* 'The first musketeer is Athos! Repeat it!'

The children shouted the name back at him. 'Athos!'

'Porthos.'

'Porthos!' *repeated the class.*

* This famous book by Alexandre Dumas tells the adventures of a group of soldiers and friends in 17th century France.

Then the teacher noticed Salim and Jamal, coming into the classroom, late again. 'Ah, here come our own musketeers!' He threw the book angrily at Salim.

'Here, Porthos! Open it!'

The book was upside-down in Salim's hands, so Jamal tried to turn it around. 'What are you doing, Athos?' the teacher cried. The rest of the class laughed loudly as he pulled the book away from Jamal and hit him on the head with it.

* * *

Life outside school wasn't always easy either. The boys and their mother were poor, and Salim was always looking for ways to earn money.

One way of doing this was with toilets. There was an area of waste land with a row of tiny wooden buildings – these were the only toilets for many people. Salim used to sit outside one of the toilets. For a price, a customer could use the toilet, while Salim guarded the door from outside.

One day a man ran up and gave a coin urgently to Salim. He was jumping up and down. It could only mean one thing – he needed the toilet right away.

Salim knocked on the door. 'Jamal, get out of there! '

'I'm not finished,' replied Jamal calmly from inside.

'There's a customer waiting!' said Salim, knocking again. But he was too late – before Jamal could reply, the man reached for the coin he had given to Salim. 'I'll go somewhere else.' As he turned to leave, he hit Salim on the back of his head.

'You just lost me a customer!' Salim shouted at the door. He was two years older than Jamal, and he got angry when Jamal didn't do what he was told.

Suddenly, there was a sound in the distance – a helicopter. A voice shouted out, 'That's Amitabh's helicopter!'

The thought of a customer for Salim didn't mean much to

Jamal, but this was different. This was Amitabh! The good-looking actor was the most famous man in India!

Jamal loved to watch him fight and sing in his many films. Quickly, he jumped to his feet and pulled up his trousers.

The sound of the helicopter was getting louder. But when Jamal came to open the door, there was a problem. Salim had locked it from the outside, and Jamal couldn't get out!

'Salim! Open the door!' he cried, but his brother was already moving towards the helicopter with all the other children. Jamal watched them all through a hole in one of the wooden walls. What could he do?

From his pocket he pulled out a picture of Amitabh. Jamal had found this in the street outside a cinema. Now he actually had a chance to ask the star to sign the picture ... but only if Jamal could reach him.

He looked down at the hole in the ground under the toilet. The water below looked awful; the smell made him feel sick, but it was the only way Jamal could think of to escape. He took a deep breath, held his nose, and jumped into the hole ... .

* * *

A large, excited crowd was standing around Amitabh now, all shouting excitedly and pushing to get closer to the film star. Everyone wanted him to speak to them, or sign something, or even just look at them.

But when Jamal joined the crowd, people moved quickly to the side, holding their noses. The boy was covered in waste from head to toe. Jamal pushed the picture towards the film star. He had managed to keep it out of the dirt. 'Amitabh sir, please sign this for me.'

Salim watched in amazement as the film star took the photo and wrote his name on it.

Holding his precious photo up to the sun, Jamal was the happiest boy in the city.

'Amitabh!' he cried.

* * *

That night Jamal didn't care that his mother was angry. He didn't care that she made him wash over and over again until the dirt and smell were gone.

14

While Jamal was washing, Salim went outside. He soon found what he was looking for in the crowded streets of Juhu – a little shop where customers paid to watch movies.

The owner of the shop did not speak when Salim handed him the photo with Amitabh's name on it. He just picked up a few rupees and gave them to the boy.

When Jamal found out what his brother had done, he fought back angry tears. 'That was my *photo!' he shouted. 'Amitabh signed it for me! I'll never get another!'*

Salim didn't care. 'I got a good price for it,' he said.

'But it was mine*!' cried Jamal, unhappily.*

Salim wasn't listening. He was already walking away, leaving his younger brother alone in the busy street.

✳ ✳ ✳

Now, years later, sitting under the studio lights, Jamal couldn't believe that he had been asked about the same famous actor.

'The answer is A,' he said. 'Amitabh Bachchan.'

As usual, Prem asked the computer to show the correct answer.

'Guess what?' he said. 'You're right!'

The presenter moved quickly to the second question. As he read it, the question and four possible answers appeared on the computer screen in front of Jamal:

> **The national emblem of India has got a picture of three lions. What is written under this picture?**

> •A: The truth alone wins   •B: Lies alone win
>
> •C: Happiness alone wins   •D: Money alone wins

The audience laughed at the last choice. The first few questions were always easy, and this one seemed even easier than usual. *Everyone* knew the answer to this question!

Jamal was silent.

'It's the most famous phrase in our country's history! Do you need help? Why don't you use a lifeline? Phone-A-Friend?' joked Prem.

'No,' answered Jamal quietly. 'Ask The Audience.'

The audience seemed surprised. Why was he using a lifeline for such an easy question?

'Please help the poor man,' Prem said to the audience. 'Press the button next to your seat if you know the answer.'

Almost everyone in the crowd pressed the button for the correct answer, A. Jamal repeated this answer to Prem.

'Congratulations!' said the presenter, when the computer showed that this was correct. 'You've just won four thousand rupees!'

CHAPTER 2
A god in the slums

There was no time to rest before the next question. This one was for sixteen thousand rupees – the quiz was getting more difficult.

Prem gave a half smile when he saw the subject of the question. 'Religion,' he told Jamal. 'Interesting.'

Jamal did not look confident. After he had asked the audience for help with the last question, nobody in the studio audience thought that he would survive much longer in the quiz. Prem read out the question:

> **In pictures of Rama, what is the god usually holding in his right hand?**
>
> **A: A flower** | **B: A knife**
> **C: A child** | **D: A bow**

Jamal was a Muslim*, and Rama was one of the gods in the Hindu† religion, but this god with the blue skin was a part of his past. Jamal had seen him years ago, on the worst day of his life ... .

✳ ✳ ✳

When they weren't at school, Jamal and Salim often went with their mother when she had to wash the family's clothes. While she worked next to all the other women in a part of the river near the train lines, the two boys enjoyed playing in the water. It felt good in the heat of the day and the boys liked the noise of the trains going past.

But that day there was a new sound – angry shouting, wild and dangerous. The boys' mother looked up to see a large crowd

---

* A person who follows the religion of Islam.

† The Hindu religion is the main religion in India (see page 82).

of men running towards the river. They were carrying big sticks and other weapons.

Jamal and Salim only looked up when they heard their mother's cry of fear as she tried to warn them.

'Run, Jamal, Salim, run!'

The crowd had almost reached them now.

'They're Muslims!' shouted a man at the front of the crowd. 'Get them!'

Suddenly Jamal was in a world of fear and hate and confusion. The crowd of men were shouting and hitting everyone they could find from this part of the city. Their eyes were filled with hate for the followers of another religion. It didn't matter to them if someone was young or old, man or woman.

People were screaming in fear and pain. Many of them ran, but Jamal's mother had not climbed out of the water: she was not going to leave her boys. She turned towards them, shouting at them to get away, to save themselves. Salim was trying to lift his younger brother out of the water, but Jamal could not take his eyes, wide with fear, from their mother.

He saw her turn around just as one of the attackers hit her on the head with a heavy stick. She fell back into the dark water.

Once the two boys had climbed out, Jamal looked back at his mother, lying, unmoving, in the water. But Salim knew that they had to get to safety, and he pulled Jamal away.

The boys ran into the narrow, crowded streets of Juhu, pushing their way past all the others who wanted to escape. The crowd of attackers was moving further into the area. There was the sound of breaking glass, then an explosion. Some of the houses were on fire now.

Too afraid to slow down, the two brothers turned one corner, then another. They found themselves in a tiny back street, but they were not alone. Someone was looking at them – a young boy whose body was blue from head to toe. His hair was long and there was a single circle of red paint above his eyes, just like the Hindu god, Rama. He just stood there, a bow in one hand, as if he was made of stone. Was it for some kind of Hindu celebration? Jamal and Salim had no idea.

They could still hear angry shouts behind them, but here the boy who was dressed like a god was just looking back at them without moving. It was like a dream.

And then the dream was broken, and the two boys were running again, back into the busy streets. They ran past a man whose clothes were on fire, past a young girl whose eyes were lost and afraid.

'Come with us!' shouted Jamal to the girl, still running.

The three children raced out of the slum and onto a main road, where a group of policemen sat in the back of a van. The boys ran to them, but the policemen were more interested in their card game than the problems of two slumdogs.

'Go away!' one of the policemen shouted, waving a stick towards the boys. The others laughed and continued smoking *their cigarettes. 'Are you deaf? I said, go away!'*

Salim understood that nobody was going to help them; they had to look after themselves. He turned and ran. Jamal remembered the girl, who was watching them now with big eyes from the other side of the road.

'Come on!' he shouted to her.

* * *

As the sun went down, the two brothers looked down at Juhu from the top of a hill. Half of the buildings were on fire now. The boys could still hear cries of pain and sadness on the wind. They had spent all of their lives in the slum; everybody they had ever known lived there. Now their home was gone, their mother was dead. Their old life in Juhu was over.

That night the rain fell – the heaviest Jamal had ever seen. The two boys found a place to sleep, inside a large metal container.

Wet and cold, they tried to get comfortable on the hard floor. Jamal looked outside. The girl who had followed them was still there. She stood, silent and alone in the heavy rain, just looking at them.

'Go away!' Salim shouted at her. 'The guard will see her and then find us,' he explained to his younger brother.

'Let her in,' answered Jamal. 'She could be the third musketeer.'

'I'm the oldest in this family now, and I say she's not coming in,' said Salim. He lay down with his back to Jamal. 'Anyway, we don't even know the name of the third musketeer.'

But Jamal could not sleep, knowing that the girl was standing there, alone and afraid in the rain. At last he called to her, 'Come over here.'

The girl joined them, grateful to be out of the rain. She sat with her back against the metal wall.

'Where's your mother?' asked Jamal.

The girl just shook her head in answer. Drops of rain fell from her hair and face.

'Your father?'

Another silent shake of the head. Jamal understood what this meant; the girl's parents were gone.

'I'm Jamal,' he said. He pointed at the older boy, who was still lying with his back to them. 'This is my brother, Salim.'

'I'm Latika,' said the girl.

'You can stay here, if you want,' said Jamal kindly.

The girl lay down on the cold metal floor. 'Thank you, Jamal.'

Next to them in the darkness, Salim lay with his eyes open and listened. Outside the rain continued to pour as if it was trying to wash away everything that had happened that day.

* * *

Now, years later, Prem was looking at Jamal, waiting for an answer. Jamal was lost in his thoughts, once again remembering the day when his mother died. He could see everything, hear every cry of pain and anger from that terrible day. He could picture the boy dressed as Rama very clearly.

'The answer is D ... a bow,' said Jamal. 'Rama is holding a bow in his hand.'

'Final answer?' Prem's face was serious.

'Final answer.'

Prem asked the computer to show the correct answer; moments later a green light appeared on answer D.

'You've just won sixteen thousand rupees,' Prem told him, holding out his hand in congratulations. 'Well done, my friend.'

Jamal could not smile. He wished that he *hadn't* known the answer; he had paid too big a price for the knowledge.

Prem was speaking to the studio audience again. 'It's time for a break,' he said. 'We'll be back after these advertisements!'

As the music played, Jamal was in sudden darkness on the studio floor. Prem was on his feet. He wasn't smiling now, as he said to Jamal, 'You got lucky, huh? If I were you, I'd take the money and run. You'll never get the next answer right.'

CHAPTER 3
A song in the night

'Welcome back to the show!' said Prem Kumar over the sound of the audience and the programme's music. With the cameras on him again, the professional smile was back in place on the presenter's face.

'Our contestant, Jamal Malik, a call centre assistant from Mumbai, is on sixteen thousand rupees and has already used one lifeline – Ask The Audience.' His eyes met Jamal's. 'So, my friend, you've reached the serious money. Shall we play?'

'Yes.'

The next question appeared on the computer screen:

> **Which famous Indian poet wrote the song 'Chalo Ri Murali'?**

Prem began to read out the four possible answers ... .

* * *

After that terrible last day in Juhu, life was hard for Jamal, Salim and Latika, with no parents and no home. Like so many other homeless children, they found themselves at last in the huge city dump. Here there were mountains of rubbish that seemed to go on forever. Every day trucks brought more and more rubbish, while the city's homeless children worked in the sun and searched the dump for food and anything useful. Life here was an unending fight to survive.

It was Latika who saw the yellow van arrive. She was standing on the top of a huge pile of rubbish, looking through the bags. She saw the word ORPHANAGE on the side of the van, and watched as a man wearing sunglasses got out.

Jamal and Salim were lying inside a tent that they had made themselves from things at the dump. They were trying to ignore the flies and the heat and the noise of the trucks and wild dogs.

They heard footsteps coming closer and then the man's voice.
'Hello?'

Jamal sat up to see the man from the van bending down to look into their tent.

'It's hot, huh?'

The man smiled as he opened two bottles of ice cold drinks and handed them to the boys. Jamal and Salim couldn't believe their luck. No one ever gave them anything … .

* * *

When the yellow van drove away from the dump, it was full of children, including Jamal, Salim and Latika. It took them all the way to the hills at the edge of the city.

Jamal looked through the window and saw a camp site in the woods, with children everywhere playing and shouting. The children in the van could not contain their excitement: was this going to be the start of a new life for them?

Minutes later they were sitting at a long table, eating their first real meal in a long, long time. They pushed the food hungrily into their mouths.

Maman, the man who had brought them from the dump to this orphanage, was walking around chatting to the children.

Watching him, Jamal said, 'From the way he's taking care of us, he must be a good man.'

Arvind, a younger boy who had come with them from the dump, asked, 'But why are we not allowed to talk to the other children?'

Nobody had an answer, not even Salim. Anyway, the only important question on their minds was, were they allowed to have more food?

* * *

As it grew dark, the children of the orphanage sat around an open fire. The new children from the city dump had been told to stand in a line to sing an old Indian song.

Maman stood in front of them. 'Arvind?' he said. The little boy stepped forward and began to sing. Maman closed his eyes and listened to the boy's clear voice.

'Very good, Arvind,' he smiled. 'Very good.'

It was Salim's turn next. He threw back his shoulders and sang as loudly and confidently as he could. It was terrible! Salim couldn't sing, and all the children began to laugh.

Salim did not share the joke. Angrily, he turned and pushed Latika hard. 'I'll kill you for laughing at me!'

Maman's huge assistant, Punnoose, pulled the boy away. 'Get off her!' he said, throwing Salim to the ground.

But Salim could not turn off his anger so easily. He turned to face Punnoose. 'Don't touch me!' he shouted. 'You big, fat tree!'

Then he ran at the large man and started hitting and hitting. Punnoose just picked Salim up by the arms and lifted him into the air.

Maman smiled at the stream of angry words from Salim's mouth. 'Punnoose, I think you've found your dog,' he said with a cold laugh.

* * *

The children soon learned what 'Punnoose's dog' was expected to do.

At the start of the day the children were driven into the city. They got out under a bridge. Ignoring the sound of traffic over their heads, the children played and chatted with each other. Only Salim sat away from the others, in the passenger seat of Punnoose's van. His eyes narrowed when he saw Jamal and Latika, together as usual.

'OK, get to work,' Punnoose told him.

Salim jumped out of the van and started towards the other children. 'Do you think you're on holiday?' he shouted. He hit one boy across the back of the head. 'What are you laughing at?'

Now that he had the group's attention, he pointed to a young girl who held a tiny baby in her arms. 'Give me that,' Salim ordered.

The baby began to cry as soon as she was in Salim's arms. 'Shut up!' he shouted.

'Brother Salim,' began Jamal, but Salim did not listen.

'What's wrong, little brother? Have you got a problem?' he pushed the baby towards Latika. 'Here! Take the baby.'

'I don't want her,' said Latika.

'It's for your own good,' said Salim. 'You get double the money if you're holding a baby.'

Latika still didn't move.

'She said she doesn't want her,' said Jamal.

'Shut up, Jamal!' Salim looked back down at Latika. 'Take her now, or I'll drop her.'

He pretended to drop the crying baby and Latika held out her hands to catch her. Salim laughed, then turned to the other

26

children. 'Come on!' he shouted. 'Get to work!'

The children ran out into the busy city, bowls in their hands. This was their 'work': all day long they had to hold out their bowls and beg for money. Most people ignored them, just walking past or driving away. Some threw a few coins in the children's direction.

* * *

Weeks passed, and the children began to know the daily pattern of their new life too well – begging in the city during the day, and then back to the orphanage at night.

But one night, the routine changed. Maman asked to hear Arvind sing again. None of the other children were there; only Punnoose, Salim and an older man who Salim had never seen before.

By the light of a single lamp, these men sat and listened to the boy. His voice had improved, and he had learned many ancient, traditional Indian songs. He started singing one by Surdas, a famous Indian poet.

Maman held up one hand for Arvind to stop. 'Very good,' he said. 'I'm happy.' He turned to the older man, who had arrived at the camp that evening. 'He's ready.'

The man didn't take his eyes from the fire. 'I'm ready, too.'

Salim just watched as Punnoose poured some liquid from a bottle onto a bit of cloth. Walking up behind Arvind, the big man held this cloth over the boy's mouth. Arvind tried to fight, but Punnoose was much too big and strong; after a few seconds, the boy lay still. He was unconscious.

The older stranger had opened a little metal box and taken out a spoon. Sitting at the fire, he heated some liquid in the spoon. Then he carried this carefully to Arvind's body.

Salim watched, hardly able to believe what was going to happen. But then the old man poured the boiling liquid from the spoon onto Arvind's eyes. He was blinding the boy!

Salim fell to his knees in shock, feeling sick. Maman had just watched everything quietly. For him, this was just another business matter.

'Salim,' he said calmly. 'Bring Jamal now.'

Salim did not move; he felt as if he couldn't move. They had blinded Arvind, and now they were going to blind his little brother!

'Bring Jamal!' repeated Maman, the anger beginning to rise in his voice.

Still Salim didn't move. Maman came closer to him. 'Listen, kid. It's time for you to decide.' He bent down until he was level with Salim. 'Do you want the life of a slumdog or the life of a man, huh? Your destiny is in your hands. You can be a real man, like me. Or ...'

Salim looked into the man's dark eyes. 'I understand,' he said quietly.

Maman smiled. 'Good. Go and get Jamal.'

✳ ✳ ✳

As usual, Jamal was with Latika. While Salim had been working as Punnoose's 'dog', the other two 'musketeers' had become closer and closer. They were sitting and talking now, while most of the other children were asleep.

'I just need Maman to like my singing,' Jamal was telling the girl. 'Then we'll be rich, Latika.'

'And then what?' she asked. 'Can we stop begging?'

'Begging?' said Jamal. 'We'll live in a big house in the nicest part of the city! You, me and Salim – the Three Musketeers!'

'Really?'

Yes!' Jamal jumped up and began to dance. 'Latika, dance with me!'

The girl laughed happily. 'I hope you sing better than you dance!'

A voice from the darkness called out, 'Jamal!'

It was Salim. Jamal smiled in excitement. 'It's my turn to sing!'

'Good luck. Sing well!' said Latika, shaking his hand.

As the two boys walked in darkness towards Maman, Jamal didn't notice how quiet and serious his brother was. Only Salim knew Maman's terrible plans for Jamal.

'This is it, big brother,' said Jamal excitedly. 'The big time!'

'Athos,' said Salim softly.

'Porthos?' Jamal was surprised. His brother never used the old names from The Three Musketeers. *So why was he using them now? Was it some kind of message?*

'Listen for my word,' Salim said quietly.

Maman was waiting for them. He gave the younger boy a big smile. 'Jamal! It's time to become professional.'

'Really?' said the boy, still excited.

'First let's hear the famous song by Surdas, "Chalo Ri Murali". That's my favourite.'

Jamal began to sing, but he stopped after the first line and held out an open hand. 'Fifty rupees, please. I'm a professional now!'

Maman laughed at the joke and threw a bank note at the boy.

Now Jamal sang as well as he could, with thoughts of money and success flying around his mind. He did not pay any attention to Punnoose or the old man at the fire.

Punnoose waved Salim over. He wanted Salim to get the cloth ready to put over Jamal's mouth. Salim took the bottle. Then suddenly, he threw the liquid right into Punnoose's face.

'Argh!' the big man cried out in pain and fell back.

'Quick, Jamal! Run!' shouted Salim.

Jamal did not understand what was happening, but he followed his brother into the darkness of the trees all around the camp. Latika had been hiding and watching everything – and she ran after them.

'Jamal!' she cried into the night.

Maman and the other men were running after the children too, shining bright lights into the thick forest.

'Get them!' shouted Maman angrily.

The three children were breathing hard, but they knew that they could not slow down. They could hear the sounds of a train ahead of them. Making themselves go even faster, they ran out of the woods. The train was leaving. If they could only reach it ... . Behind them they could hear Maman's angry voice.

Salim reached the train first, pulling himself up into an empty car.

Jamal ran. His legs hurt, his breath burned in his chest. But Salim was reaching a hand out for him. Moments later, Jamal was on the train, too.

Salim looked back at Latika. She was the youngest and smallest of the three children, and she was also the slowest. She ran as hard as she could, reaching out for Salim's hand. 'Jamal!' she screamed.

Salim's hand closed around the girl's. But instead of pulling her up into the train, he let go of her hand.

Unable to run any more, Latika stopped and watched as the train moved away from her. Maman and his men were going to be there soon; there was no way to escape them.

'What happened?' cried Jamal on the train. He wanted to jump off and run back. 'We've got to go back for her. We've got to!'

But Salim held him down. 'If we go back, we're dead!' he shouted. 'He was going to take out your eyes with a spoon!'

At last Jamal stopped fighting.

'Don't worry about her,' continued Salim. 'She'll be fine. She always is.'

Jamal did not speak. He couldn't imagine life without Latika. The train continued into the black night, taking the two brothers into an uncertain future.

* * *

The television studio was silent. In his mind Jamal could still hear the songs of the orphanage children, while Maman sat in the firelight and smiled.

'The answer is Surdas,' he said.

Prem Kumar stared at him. How could a *chai-wallah* know about poetry? 'Is that your final answer?'

Jamal returned the stare. How could the presenter know the terrible story of how Jamal had learned this information?

'Yes, final answer.'

The seconds seemed to stretch into hours, before Prem smiled again and cried, 'You're right!'

The crowd went wild. They were starting to realise that something special was happening here tonight with this *chai-wallah* from Mumbai.

CHAPTER 4
Looking for Latika

It was the start of a new life for the brothers – a life on the trains. They crossed all over the country, from Rajastan in the north, to Calcutta in the south, and back. Soon they hardly even noticed the movement of the trains. Sometimes the boys rode on top of passenger trains; at other times they hid inside empty cars with other homeless travellers. If a train guard found them, he always threw them off the train, but this wasn't a problem. There were always other trains to climb on.

But Jamal did not stop thinking about Latika. What had happened to her? How was she now? He relived the escape from Maman again and again in his mind. He wished that he had done something different; he wished that Latika was still with them.

But there were many other things to think of. The boys were on their own: if they didn't want to be hungry, they had to get their own food. Salim was still good at making money. Sometimes they sold things to passengers for money; at other times they stole food from the tables of rich families travelling on the trains.

This was their life for years, always on the move. They were used to the routines of daily life on the trains. But one day this life ended suddenly, when they were thrown off the train yet again. As usual, they landed on the hard ground next to the train line. But, when Jamal sat up, he was looking at something very different from anything he'd ever seen before.

'Am I imagining that?' asked Jamal in wonder. 'Or have we died?'

He was looking at a beautiful white building in the distance. The two boys didn't know it, but this was one of the most famous buildings in the world, the Taj Mahal. Every year

thousands of tourists came to see its beauty for themselves.

'You are not dead, Jamal,' said Salim.

As they went closer, the boys saw there were tourists everywhere looking around the building. Groups of visitors followed tour guides, who told them fact after fact about the building and its long history.

Jamal was just standing looking around, when two middle-aged tourists walked up to him.

'Please, what time is the next tour?' asked the woman. She spoke English but with a strong German accent. Looking over his shoulder, Jamal realised that these tourists thought he was a tour guide!

'Could you show us around now?' continued the woman. 'Of course, we know that it will cost more for just the two of us.'

Her husband pushed some bank notes at Jamal. He thought quickly. Taking the money, he said, 'Of course. Please follow me.'

It was the start of the worst tour ever of the Taj Mahal! Jamal repeated the few facts that he had heard from the real tour guides; everything else was a lie. He even explained how the first plan was for the Taj Mahal to be a hotel!

'There's nothing about the plans for a hotel in the guide book,' said the German woman, looking confused.

Jamal looked at her calmly. 'The guide book was written by lazy Indian beggars!' he explained.

This was his first time as a tour guide at the Taj Mahal, but it wasn't the last. Over the next few months, Jamal showed more and more tourists around the famous building. The two brothers had other ways of making money, too: it was a rule that visitors to the Taj Mahal had to take their shoes off. The brothers used to steal the shoes and then sell them later. At the end of the day, they slept in a camp for the homeless. Although they were now living in the north of India, far from Juhu, the boys were still living in a slum.

During the days, Jamal continued to show tourists around. He took an American couple to the river to see the hundreds of Indian women there, washing clothes in the water. The couple's Indian driver parked his car and followed the tourists and their guide.

As soon as they were out of sight, Salim and some other street kids went up to the car. Within minutes, they had taken everything they could sell – even the wheels!

When the tourists returned, the American man said, 'Wow! What happened here?'

The driver had a good idea what had happened and he was angry. He began to hit Jamal on the head, sure that the young guide knew about the boys' plan. He pushed Jamal to the ground and began to kick him.

'No!' cried the American woman. But the driver didn't stop until the woman's husband pulled him away.

'You said you wanted to see the real India?' Jamal shouted up at the tourists, holding his head in pain. 'Well, here it is!'

'Well, here is a bit of the real America, son,' said the woman proudly.

Her husband pulled a bank note from his pocket and handed it to Jamal – a hundred-dollar bill!

* * *

That night something special was happening outside the Taj Mahal. Jamal could hear the sound of classical music. There was a show of some kind. Hundreds of people had come in their finest clothes to watch an opera* at this special place.

For Salim and the other homeless children this was a chance to steal some money from the pockets of the rich. But Jamal did not join them. There was something about the music that touched him.

He just stopped and watched. He didn't know the story of the opera, but he could understand what was happening in it now. A man was sitting and holding the body of his dead wife. His song was the saddest, most beautiful thing Jamal had ever heard.

As he listened, Jamal knew something in his heart. He had to go back to Mumbai; he had to go back for Latika.

* * *

In the television studio, Prem read out the next question:

> **On an American one hundred-dollar bill, there is a picture of which American politician?**

- **A:** George Washington
- **B:** Franklin Roosevelt
- **C:** Benjamin Franklin
- **D:** Abraham Lincoln

The presenter did not hide his smile. 'Do you get a lot of hundred-dollar bills in your job, Jamal?'

Jamal was happy to play this game, too. 'It's the minimum tip for my work,' he said. The crowd laughed, surprised that this *chai-wallah* was brave enough to answer

* A musical play in which all of the characters sing their lines.

Prem with a joke of his own.

'Now I know why my mobile phone bills are so high,' replied the presenter. It was clear that he didn't want Jamal to win the biggest laugh from the audience.

But before the audience's laughter had died, Jamal said, 'The answer is C.'

Moments later the computer showed the correct answer on the screen.

Prem was a professional, but he couldn't quite hide his look of surprise. 'You have just won one *million* rupees!'

* * *

Jamal and Salim had just been boys when they ran away from Mumbai; when they returned to the city now, years later, they were teenagers. Mumbai had changed, too. There was lots of new building going on all over the city; many of the old places the boys had known – Juhu, their old slum, the orphanage – were gone. But in many ways the city was unchanged. It was still a place where millions of the poor had to fight to live and survive.

Jamal spent long days looking for Latika, walking all over the city, but nobody knew anyone with that name. Jamal found a job working in a hotel kitchen so that he and Salim could buy food.

Salim wasn't happy to be back in the city. 'We left a good life behind at the Taj,' he said angrily.

'We came back to find Latika,' Jamal reminded him.

'No, you came back for her, Jamal – I didn't. I don't care about her! There are nineteen million people in this city. Forget her. She's history!'

But Salim was wrong. A few days later, when Jamal was crossing under a busy road, he passed a beggar singing for money. Jamal paused – this was a face he remembered from his past. It was Arvind, the boy who had been blinded by Maman years ago.

Jamal looked into the young beggar's sightless eyes. Arvind stopped singing and said, 'Those who help others will find luck themselves, sir.'

Without a word, Jamal handed his old friend the one-hundred dollar bill. Arvind held it to his face and breathed in.

'Dollars!' he said. 'How much?'

'One hundred,' said Jamal.

'Do you think I'm stupid?'

'It's true,' said Jamal. 'I promise you.'

'What's on this note?' asked Arvind. 'Whose picture?'

Jamal looked down at the note. 'It's an old man. He's got no hair on top of his head but long hair at the sides, like a girl.'

Arvind smiled, knowing now that this was the truth. 'It's Benjamin Franklin*,' he said. Arvind reached up to touch Jamal's face; he knew Jamal's voice. He had met his old friend

* A writer and thinker who played an important part in the birth of the United States of America.

again. 'So you're a big guy now, Jamal? I'm happy for you.'

Looking at the beggar's sightless eyes, Jamal didn't know what to say. The words didn't seem enough, but he managed, 'I'm sorry, Arvind.'

The beggar spoke without anger. 'You were saved, my friend. I wasn't so lucky – that's the only difference.'

Jamal took a deep breath. 'Arvind, I'm trying to find Latika.'

Arvind understood. 'Keep away!' he said. 'Maman never forgets. He'll kill you!'

But Jamal had to know. 'She's alive, isn't she?'

'She's on Pila Street,' said Arvind. 'They call her Cherry now.'

Jamal took a last look at his old friend and the terrible destiny he himself had only just avoided. 'Thanks,' he whispered.

As he ran off, Arvind's voice followed him. 'I'll sing for you at your funeral!'

CHAPTER 5
The man with the Colt 45

Pila Street was dark and narrow. Jamal and Salim had to push their way through crowds of men there that night. In the buildings, women stood in doors or at upstairs windows, waiting for customers. Pila Street was a place where women could be bought and sold. It seemed to Jamal to be a place without hope or happiness.

At each house he stopped and asked for a girl called 'Cherry'. It took a long time, but finally one woman pointed down the street. The boys went inside a tiny house and walked down a narrow hall with cubicles on each side. They could hear music from the end of the corridor, and through the open door Jamal could see a young woman dancing to it.

When he came closer, Jamal's heart jumped. It was Latika! Of course, she was older – about thirteen years old – and she was

dressed in fine clothes and lots of jewellery. She looked beautiful as she danced around and around to the music, but she seemed to find no happiness in it. A teacher sat at the back of the room shouting instructions.

'Is it her?' Salim joined his brother at the door. 'Wow, she's sexy.'

Jamal couldn't wait any longer. He pushed his way into the room shouting, 'Latika!'

Latika turned round. Her eyes lit up with happiness and surprise when she recognised Jamal.

'Look who we have here,' said a man from the door. They knew that voice too well – it was Maman. He spoke calmly, but they could hear the anger deep down. 'Hello again, Jamal, Salim. I never forget a face ... especially one that I own.'

Behind him Punnoose stared at the boys with a look of hate. His face still had the scars from the liquid that Salim had thrown at him that night, years ago.

Maman gave a low, dark laugh. 'Did you really think that you could just walk in and take my prize away? Do you have any idea how much men will pay for her?'

He turned to the dance teacher. 'Please continue now.' Then to Punnoose, 'Get them out of here!'

But Punnoose didn't move. He had seen Salim pull something from his pocket. Salim was pointing a revolver straight at him!

Jamal couldn't believe his eyes. He had no idea that his brother was carrying a gun.

'Get over there!' cried Salim to the men.

The smile had not left Maman's face. 'Don't do anything stupid,' he laughed. He spoke as if he was talking to a small child. 'Heavy, isn't it? Give it to me.'

Salim was moving back towards the wall. 'On your knees,' he cried. 'Down!'

Maman and the other two men got on their knees.

'Money,' Salim said.

'You can have money,' Maman said quickly. He pulled out all the notes and coins from his pockets and threw them on the floor. 'See?'

Maman sounded more nervous now. There was something about the cold look in Salim's eye that he recognised – and it frightened him. Maman had seen the same thing when he looked at himself in the mirror.

'Take the money,' he said quickly. 'Leave with your friend and we'll forget all about this. OK?'

'But Maman never forgets,' answered Salim. He was holding a pillow over the end of the gun now, just centimetres from the man's head. 'Isn't that right?'

'I can make an exception,' Maman said, and Jamal could hear the fear behind his false smile.

'I can't take that chance, Maman,' said Salim. 'Sorry.'

There was just a second for Maman to understand what Salim meant by this apology, and then Salim fired. It was impossible to miss from such a short distance. Maman fell back, dead.

Jamal looked away in shock, hands on his ears, unable to believe what had happened. While Salim pointed the gun at the other men, Latika quickly picked up the money from the floor in front of Maman's body.

'Jamal!' shouted Salim urgently. 'Come on! Let's go!'

And then the three of them ran out into the night. Jamal followed the other two. He had wanted them to be together again – the 'three musketeers' from all those years ago! – but not like this ... .

* * *

Jamal knew about a hotel that was empty. There was only one guard there and he was sleeping. It was easy for the three to get past him and run upstairs to one of the rooms.

Salim was in a good mood – Maman had been carrying a lot of money with him. Salim had bought some strong drink to celebrate. He was already drinking it from the bottle.

He could hear Jamal and Latika talking in the other room. His brother had what he wanted — he had found Latika — but Salim could not share his brother's happiness.

Salim walked out into the night. It was late, but the streets of Mumbai were never quiet. He knew where to go. He found the group of men upstairs in a bar playing cards.

'I'm looking for Javed.'

'He's not looking for you,' answered one of the men without interest. They went back to their game.

For the second time that day, Salim pulled out the gun. The men didn't move; all eyes were on the gun.

'I killed Maman,' he told them. 'And I'll kill you, too. Easy.'

Suddenly a voice from behind Salim said, 'You killed Maman?'

It was Javed. Since Salim and his brother had been small boys, Javed had been the biggest crime boss in Juhu. He looked Salim up and down, then said, 'My enemy's enemy is a friend, no? Come here, friend.'

Salim put his gun away and walked up to Javed.

'I've been looking for someone like you,' said Javed.

And so Salim's life of crime began.

✳ ✳ ✳

Jamal and Latika lay side by side in the dark of the hotel room. They had been talking for hours.

'You came back for me,' Latika said, gratefully. 'I thought you'd forgotten me.'

'I never forgot ... not for one moment.' Jamal looked at the girl who he had dreamed about for so long. 'I knew I'd find you. It's our destiny.'

'Destiny,' repeated Latika. She knew that her own destiny had changed that day. 'Thank you,' she said.

They fell asleep next to each other, happy to be together again for the first time in years. When Jamal woke up, there was someone standing over them in the dark. It was Salim.

He held his hand out to Latika. 'Come.'

Jamal sat up. 'You've had a lot to drink, brother.'

But Salim's voice was cold and hard. 'I am the big brother. I am the boss. For once, you do as I say. Now get out!'

He turned his attention back to Latika. 'Come on. I saved your life, didn't I?'

This was too much for Jamal. He threw himself at his brother, shouting and hitting. But Salim was bigger and stronger. He pushed Jamal – still kicking and shouting – out into the hall and shut the door.

'Salim!' Jamal shouted, hitting the door with his hand.

The door opened, and Salim stood there, pointing the gun at Jamal.

'Shut up! The man with the Colt 45* in his hand says SHUT UP! Go now, or I will shoot you right between the eyes.'

Jamal just stood there, unable to believe his own brother was doing this. Salim had already shot and killed one man that day. Surely it wasn't possible that he could shoot his own brother?

* A type of revolver.

Jamal was no longer sure.

'I'm giving you five seconds,' said Salim. 'One, two ...'

A hand reached out from behind Salim and slowly pushed his arm down. It was Latika.

'Go, Jamal,' she said sadly, knowing that this was the only way to save his life. 'Go.'

Then Salim closed the door and Jamal was left standing alone in the hall.

* * *

As he asked the next question, Prem held his hand like a gun and pointed it straight at Jamal.

> ### Who invented the revolver?
>
> **A: Samuel Colt**   **B: Bruce Browning**
>
> **C: Dan Wesson**   **D: James Revolver**

Jamal did not even pause. 'Samuel Colt.'

'Final answer?'

Jamal looked back into the presenter's eyes. He remembered the terrible sound of the gun in that room on Pila Street; he remembered looking in shock at the weapon in his brother's hand; he remembered Maman's lifeless body falling to the floor.

'Final answer,' he said.

Prem was not making jokes now – this was too serious, the question was for too much money.

'Jamal Malik,' the presenter said. 'You're on a dream run. My heart says that you're going to win more.' He took a breath. 'Computer, show us the correct answer.'

He looked down at the screen, then shouted, 'I was right! The *chai-wallah* has done it again!'

Jamal listened as the crowd cheered wildly. 'Amazing!' cried Prem, looking at him in total disbelief.

CHAPTER 6
A world away

When Jamal returned to the hotel the next day, Salim and Latika were gone. There was no message for him. For the first time in his life, Jamal was completely on his own.

Five years passed, and still Jamal heard nothing from his brother or Latika. He lived in a tiny wooden home in the slums. He was eighteen years old when he got a job as a chai-wallah *in a call centre.*

The call centre workers were given lessons about British culture and place names. This was so that someone from Britain didn't know that the person they were talking to on the phone was in a different country, thousands of miles away. Jamal's job wasn't important enough for him to receive these lessons, but he still listened and watched carefully while he was bringing everyone their tea.

During one lesson, the teacher held up a magazine with a picture of a young British TV actress on the cover and said, 'Now for the biggest news in England this week. Kat is back in EastEnders*!'

'She came back long ago!' said one of the workers.

'Jamal?' the teacher said, looking at him as he walked around serving tea.

'Well, she came back, then she went away again when her boyfriend left her,' explained Jamal. 'Now she's back again.'

The teacher smiled. 'You see?' she told the workers. 'The chai-wallah *knows more than you do!'*

In the rest of the office, hundreds of workers sat at desks speaking into head-sets. The air was filled with voices, having different telephone conversations with people in Britain. All

---

* A popular British television programme about the everyday lives of people in the east of London.

around the room there were signs with British place names to help the workers remember them. There were photos of bright-red London buses and telephone boxes, stars from British TV, and photos of the British countryside all around the walls. The photos showed a completely different world from Mumbai.

'Jamal!' a worker called Ali waved him over. 'Come and take my place!'

Jamal looked worried – if the manager saw him, he would be in big trouble.

'Please!' begged Ali. 'It's my turn to call Who Wants To Be A Millionaire?.*'*

'OK, just for two minutes,' said Jamal, sitting down.

Ali ran off to watch to watch the television in the next room. The moment the show's presenter, Prem, asked new contestants to call in so that they could take part in the show, Ali shouted to all of the other workers. Immediately, they began hitting the numbers on their phones. All of them wanted to be in the show and win some big money – enough to leave the boring work at the call centre behind and never return.

Jamal sat in front of Ali's computer. He pressed a button, and suddenly a question came up on the screen. 'What name are you looking for?'

Quickly Jamal's hands moved over the keys and he wrote Latika *in the empty box. He hit the button and thousands of names and telephone numbers appeared on the screen.*

Jamal tried again, this time putting in the name Salim K. Malik. *Now there were just fifteen numbers on the screen.*

Jamal chose the first number and phoned it.

'Yes?' said a man's voice.

'Salim?' Jamal said into the head-set's microphone.

'Who's this?' asked the man angrily. 'Do you know what time it is?'

Before the man could say anything else, Jamal ended the call with the push of a button.

He tried the next number on the list – with the same result – but the third voice was one that he knew well.

'Hello,' said his brother. 'Who is this?'

Jamal said what he had heard all the other workers say. 'I'm calling from your mobile phone company. We'd like to give you our special offer for friends and ...' Jamal paused, '... family.'

'Jamal? Is that you, brother?' Salim's voice went from unsure to happy. 'I thought that you were dead or something. Listen, we had to leave that night: Maman's guys were searching the hotel. Jamal? Say something, please!'

The last time they had spoken, Salim had pointed a gun at him. Now, with difficulty, Jamal said, 'Hello, Salim.'

* * *

The questions kept on coming at Jamal on *Who Wants To Be A Millionaire?*. The next one brought back memories from those long hours working at the call centre.

> **Cambridge Circus* is in which British city?**
>
> **A: Oxford**   **B: Leeds**
>
> **C: Cambridge**   **D: London**

Jamal looked at the four possible answers. Although he had never travelled outside India, he had heard these names so many times at the call centre.

'It isn't Cambridge,' he said.

'May I ask why?' asked Prem.

'Too obvious.' Jamal looked thoughtful. 'There's a famous boat race in London between Oxford and Cambridge. And there's an Oxford Circus in London, too. So there's probably a Cambridge Circus too, no? I'll go for

---

* An open, round area where two or more roads meet.

answer D, London!'

Prem shook his head in disbelief again as the computer showed the correct answer. 'Jamal Malik, you're ... ABSOLUTELY RIGHT!'

Again, the crowd went wild. The *chai-wallah* had won two and a half million rupees!

'It's getting hot in here,' said Prem, as he handed Jamal a cheque for the money.

'Are you nervous?' Jamal asked.

For just a moment, the presenter couldn't hide the look of anger on his face. 'Am *I* nervous? It's *you* who is in the hot seat, my friend.'

* * *

Salim had arranged to meet his brother at a building site. The building wasn't finished yet, but Jamal took the builders' lift up to the top. Salim was there, waiting for him.

Salim looked very different. He was a man now. He wore expensive clothes and sunglasses, and there was a gold watch on his wrist.

'Jamal?' Salim walked towards his younger brother with open arms and a smile on his face. 'God is good!'

Jamal's mood was very different. As his older brother came closer, Jamal hit him in the face. Salim fell to the ground.

He looked up at his brother. 'We had to escape from Maman's men. They came to the hotel,' he said. 'I tried to leave a message for you.'

'That's a lie!' cried Jamal. 'There was no message!' His eyes met Salim's. 'I will never *forgive you!'*

Salim looked down. 'I know,' he said quietly.

* * *

Later, when Jamal had calmed down, the two brothers sat together and looked down over the edge at the city below.

Salim pointed at one area. 'That used to be Juhu, our old slum. Can you believe that? Now it's all business. India is at the centre of the world, brother. And I? I am at the centre of the centre.' He waved a hand over the city. 'This is all Javed's.'

'You work for Javed?' Jamal remembered Javed well. Clearly, Javed had become more and more powerful in the years since then.

'Come on,' said Salim, waving his cigarette impatiently. 'Who else could save us from Maman's men?'

Jamal was beginning to understand the life his older brother was living now. 'What do you do for him?'

'Anything he asks.'

The phone in Salim's pocket started to ring. Salim looked down at the screen. 'That's Javed,' he said. 'I've got to go.'

As he stood up, he gave Jamal a card with his number on it. 'What's this for?' asked Jamal.

'Do you think I'm going to let you out of my sight again, younger brother? You will stay with me now.'

But Jamal couldn't go yet – not until he had asked the

question that he had waited years to ask. 'Salim, where is Latika?'

'You're *still looking for her?*' Salim could not believe his ears. 'She's gone – long gone. Now go, go to my place!'

* * *

Jamal moved into Salim's apartment, but the relationship was not the same now. His brother was very different from the Salim Jamal remembered. Jamal didn't know exactly what his brother did for Javed, but he could guess that it had to do with crime. He never went anywhere without his gun.

Salim had changed in other ways, too. Before he left the apartment every morning, he went down on his knees and prayed.

'God, forgive me. I know that I have done bad things.'

When Salim left and went to his car, he did not know that Jamal had followed him outside.

Jumping into a taxi, Jamal told the driver to follow Salim's car. They drove all the way to a large house on the edge of the city. An electric gate opened and Salim's car disappeared inside.

Jamal paid the taxi driver and looked in through the gates. A woman was standing at a window. Her hair was longer and she was wearing expensive clothes but it was Latika. She was even more beautiful than Jamal remembered. He felt nervous but he had to see her.

Jamal walked up to the guard at the gatehouse. 'I'm the new cook,' he lied. 'Sorry I'm so late!'

The guard checked his notes. 'Nobody said anything about a new cook. We're only expecting a new dishwasher to arrive today.'

Jamal gave the man a smile. 'That's me! I'm the new dishwasher!'

Moments later he was stepping inside the huge house. It felt like another world to him with its huge rooms and expensive furniture.

Latika was standing at the top of the stairs, her eyes full of happiness and surprise. Jamal ran to her and the two old friends fell into each other's arms. 'Jamal! Look at you!'

Jamal could not let her go, not after so long. 'I found you!'

A look of worry crossed Latika's face and she turned away. 'Why are you here?'

'To see you.'

Latika shook her head. 'Well, you've seen me. Now what?'

Suddenly there was the sound of a car outside. 'Oh no!' said Latika. 'Javed is home! He'll kill you.'

At that moment Jamal understood. Latika might have escaped from Maman, but she hadn't escaped from her old life. She was dressed in the best clothes money could buy; she lived in a huge, expensive house; she slept in a bed, not on the streets. But she was still a prisoner.

Javed came into the room and looked at Latika coldly. 'First you wanted a dishwasher ... . Now you want a cook!' he said angrily, pointing at Jamal.

'No, let me explain, I ...' Latika said, her voice shaking with fear.

'Shut up!' Javed shouted.

He turned and went to the living room to watch cricket on TV. 'I'm hungry,' he said over his shoulder. 'Make me a sandwich.'

As they prepared the sandwich, Jamal whispered to Latika. 'Come away with me.'

'Where to? And what would we live on?'

Jamal only had one answer. 'Love.'

Latika said nothing. She took the sandwich to the living room. Javed waved at her to get out of the way of the screen.

As she returned to the kitchen, she shook her head. Jamal might have his romantic dreams, but she knew more about real life.

'Salim will help us,' said Jamal.

Latika looked at him in disbelief. 'Salim? You still believe in Salim?' She shook her head sadly. 'I'll be gone soon anyway. We're leaving the city.'

From the other room, Javed shouted at the television, unhappy with how the cricket was going. He bit into the sandwich.

Moments later he was back in the kitchen, throwing the plate down angrily. Clearly, the sandwich wasn't good enough for Javed, and he did not believe in giving anybody a second chance. 'This is rubbish!' he shouted at Jamal. 'Get out!'

Latika led Jamal to the door. 'Go, before he kills us both! If you want to do something for me, Jamal, just forget me.'

Jamal stopped at the door. 'No. I'll wait for you. I'll wait at the VT Station* at five o'clock every day, until you come.'

In Latika's eyes there was hope – but mostly sadness.

'I love you,' said Jamal.

Latika shook her head – she had seen too much; she knew that people needed more than just love. She did not like her life with Javed, but she had learned to accept it. She knew that there was no escape.

'So what?' she said, pushing him outside. 'It's too late for us, Jamal. Go!'

And then she closed the door.

* The largest train station in Mumbai.

CHAPTER 7
'Just trust me'

'So, Jamal,' said Prem, 'which cricketer has had the most centuries* in international cricket?'

As the presenter read out the list of possible answers, Jamal looked nervous – he didn't know anything about famous cricketers.

'Remember,' Prem reminded him, 'if you get the answer wrong, you will lose all the money you've won so far. So ... what do you want to do?'

'I want to continue playing,' said Jamal.

＊ ＊ ＊

Jamal was true to his word. Every day he finished work and went straight to VT Station. At this time of day the platforms were always crowded. Jamal was afraid that he might not see Latika in this sea of people. He found a good spot on the bridge that joined the platforms and waited.

Time passed. Jamal put his head down, losing hope. But then, just when he was going to give up, he saw her below him, standing on one of the platforms. She had come! Latika had come!

'Latika!' he cried in excitement. 'Latika!'

She heard his voice over the sound of hundreds of footsteps and conversations. She turned and looked up at him. It was a perfect moment – the sun falling on her like a light, her smile as she found Jamal's face in the crowd.

Hope flowered in Jamal's heart. But, before he could run down the stairs to take her in his arms, he saw three men running to catch Latika. One of them was Salim.

---

* A point in cricket is called a *run*; a *century* is 100 runs.

Jamal shouted again, this time to warn her. 'Latika!'

When Latika saw Javed's men coming to get her, a look of terrible fear crossed her face. She tried to run, but she had no chance. Javed's men reached her easily and began to drag her out of the station.

Jamal raced down the stairs as fast as he could. By the time he got outside, the men had pushed Latika into the back of a waiting car.

Salim was holding Latika around the neck. One of the other men was holding a large knife.

'Latika!' cried Jamal, running towards the car and banging on the window.

As it drove off, he saw one of the men run the knife across Latika's face. Javed was a man who got what he wanted; when someone broke his trust, there was a price to pay.

* * *

Before Jamal had to answer the next question, there was another break for advertisements. Jamal went to the studio toilets and hid in one of the cubicles. He needed time to think.

After a few minutes he heard someone come into the toilets. Jamal did not open the cubicle door, but moments later he heard a voice.

'A guy from the slums becomes a millionaire in one day,' said Prem Kumar. 'Do you know the only other person who's done that? *Me*. I know what you're going through. I know what it feels like.'

'I'm not going to become a millionaire,' said Jamal from behind the cubicle door. 'I don't know the answer.'

Prem laughed as he went to wash his hands. 'Come on, you can't take the money and run now. You're on the edge of history, kid.'

'I don't see what else I can do.'

'Maybe it's your destiny, my friend,' said Prem. 'I've just got a feeling that you will win this. Just trust me, Jamal – you're going to win.'

Inside the cubicle, Jamal heard the sound of a door opening. He left the cubicle, still not knowing what to do.

Then he saw the mirror where Prem had just washed his hands. It was still foggy from the hot water, and someone had written on it with their finger. It was a single letter – B.

Jamal's heart jumped. Prem must have done this. He had given Jamal the answer! But why?

* * *

Back on the studio floor, Jamal took his seat opposite Prem. Studio workers hurried around them; it was almost time for the programme to start again.

'Do the right thing,' whispered Prem, 'and in about three minutes, you will be as famous as me. And as rich as me ... .' His eyes met Jamal's. 'It's your destiny.'

The studio manager was counting down to the start of the programme. 'Ten, nine, eight ...' And then the music was playing.

'Welcome back to *Who Wants To Be A Millionaire?*!' cried Prem. 'In the chair tonight is Jamal Malik, playing now for ten million rupees. The question once again ...'

Which cricketer has had the most centuries in international cricket?

A: Sachin Tendulkar   **B:** Ricky Ponting

C: Michael Slater   **D:** Jack Hobbs

Jamal looked hard at the four names. 'I know it isn't Sachin Tendulkar*.'

'That's a start!' smiled Prem.

'I'll use a lifeline,' said Jamal. '50:50.'

'OK. Computer, take away two wrong answers, please.'

Answers A and C disappeared from the screen.

'Well, you were right about Sachin Tendulkar,' said Prem. 'That leaves you with a choice of two ... . What do you think?'

Jamal was silent.

'It's decision time,' Prem's voice was urgent. 'For ten million rupees.'

Jamal's past could not provide him with this answer, but it had given him something. It had taught him about people. He looked into the presenter's eyes. Prem was smiling, but his eyes were cold and hard.

'D,' said Jamal. 'Jack Hobbs.'

The smile disappeared from Prem's face. 'Not B? Ricky Ponting, the great Australian cricketer?'

---

* A famous Indian cricketer, born in Mumbai.

Jamal's eyes were still on the presenter. 'D.'

'You know this?' asked Prem. When Jamal shook his head slowly, the presenter insisted. 'So it could be B, Ricky Ponting?'

'Or D, Jack Hobbs ... . That's my final answer.'

Prem closed his eyes and shook his head. 'Computer, show the correct answer, please.'

Prem looked down at the screen. 'With 197 international centuries, the answer is ...' He looked up at Jamal. 'D, Jack Hobbs!'

Jamal had won an amazing ten million rupees! The audience were on their feet, shouting and cheering. They couldn't believe what had happened, and Jamal couldn't believe it either. But he knew one thing. Prem Kumar was smiling and dancing in celebration now, but Jamal knew what Prem had done. He had given Jamal the wrong answer.

Prem did not want him to win.

CHAPTER 8
The final question

It took a long time for the noise of the crowd to die down. They knew that history was being made here.

'So, are you ready for the final question, for twenty million rupees?' asked Prem.

'No,' answered Jamal. 'But ... maybe it's my destiny, no?'

Prem paused. Only he knew what Jamal meant – the presenter had tried to trick him and failed. They both knew it.

'Maybe,' said Prem quietly. He looked down at the cards in his hands. 'OK, the final question ...'

But before he could ask, a loud noise rang around the studio – it was the end of the show. The crowd gave a disappointed sound.

'What a show!' said Prem, looking straight into the camera. 'Join us tomorrow night to see if Jamal Malik has made the biggest mistake of his life by deciding to play on!'

* * *

When the producer led Jamal out of the studio, Prem was waiting in the corridor for him.

'Great show,' he said, putting his hand on Jamal's shoulder. He did not mention the incorrect answer on the bathroom mirror. He just opened the door for Jamal and said, 'See you tomorrow.'

As soon as Jamal stepped outside, someone was ready and waiting for him. Two policeman pulled a cloth bag over his head and pushed him into the back of a waiting truck. Constable Srinivas sat at the wheel, ready to drive away.

The TV producer joined Prem Kumar at the door. 'What's going on?' he asked, confused.

Prem calmly lit a cigarette. 'He's a cheat.'

'How do you know?' asked the producer.

'I gave him the wrong answer and he still got the question right!' Prem said angrily.

The producer was shocked. 'You gave him an answer?'

'Not exactly ... . Anyway, it doesn't matter.' Prem turned back towards the studio. 'This is my show ... MY show!'

* * *

That night at the police station had been the longest of Jamal's life, as Constable Srinivas asked him question after question.

Now, sitting in the Inspector's office the next morning, Jamal tried to ignore the awful hunger and thirst he felt. His body ached and he just wanted to rest, to put his head down and sleep. Although it was still early, he was already sweating in the heat. The Inspector was studying him in silence as Srinivas put the video in the video player. The air was thick with cigarette smoke.

The programme started. For Jamal this was like a bad dream, sitting at the Inspector's desk and watching himself on *Who Wants To Be A Millionaire?*.

They watched in silence as he answered the first question in the game, the one about the actor Amitabh.

'You don't have to be brilliant to know that,' said Jamal.

'I knew the answer to that one,' admitted Srinivas from the back of the room.

'See?' said Jamal. 'Like I said, you don't have to be brilliant ... .'

Immediately, Srinivas was on him, bending his arm up his back.

'Amitabh's the most famous man in India!' cried Jamal.

The Inspector ordered Srinivas off. He pointed at the screen, where Jamal was using his Ask The Audience lifeline to ask the second question, about the national emblem of India.

'My five-year old daughter could answer that question,' said the Inspector. 'What happened? Did your helper in the audience leave the studio for a minute?'

In reply, Jamal just said, 'Who stole Constable Varma's bicycle from outside the station last Thursday?'

The Inspector was surprised. 'What? You know who that was?'

Jamal smiled. 'Everyone in Juhu knows that ... even five year olds.'

The Inspector smiled, too.

When the video came to the third question – the one about Rama – Jamal explained how he knew the answer. He told the Inspector how his mother had died in Juhu that day. He told him how he and Salim had run, and how they had met Latika for the first time.

As the video of the show continued, the Inspector listened in silence to Jamal's story – the awful secret of the orphanage, the boys' escape into the night, their new life on the trains and at the Taj Mahal.

When the video came to the question about the hundred-dollar bill, the Inspector pulled a bank note out of his pocket.

'Who's on a thousand-rupee bank note?' he asked.

'I don't know.'

The Inspector waved the money in front of Jamal. 'It's Gandhi*!' His meaning was clear: how could Jamal know

* A famous Indian political leader.

the picture on an American hundred-dollar bill, but not the famous Indian leader?

'I've heard of him,' said Jamal.

The Inspector kicked Jamal's chair in anger. 'Don't try to make clever jokes, or I'll get the electricity out again,' he warned.

'Look,' said Jamal. 'They didn't ask me a question about rupees. I don't know why. Ask *them*.'

The Inspector stared hard at him. 'It's funny – you don't seem that interested in money. Explain the hundred-dollar bill.'

And so Jamal told him him about the return to Mumbai and his search for Latika. He told him about Arvind and what had happened in Pila Street. The Inspector understood now why Jamal had known who invented the revolver.

'You trouble me, slumdog,' he said. 'Admitting murder to prove that you didn't cheat in a quiz ... it's not exactly clever. Now why would you do that?'

'When somebody asks me a question, I tell them the answer,' said Jamal simply.

He continued to tell his story, finishing with the day at the VT Station when Salim and Javed's other men had dragged Latika away.

While he talked, the video continued to play. When the programme ended, the Inspector turned the television off. 'There's something believable about your story,' he said at last.

'And yet, because I'm a *chai-wallah*, a *slumdog* – you think I'm lying, right?'

'Most of you do,' said the Inspector. 'But you're not lying, Mr Malik ... You're too truthful.' He thought for a moment, then said, 'We're finished here.'

Jamal stayed in his seat. A terrible tiredness was starting to hit him. 'I don't know where they've taken Latika.' The Inspector paused at the door, listening. 'I went back to Javed's house to look for her. The house was empty. That's why I went on the programme – because I thought that she might watch.'

CHAPTER 9
The final answer

Jamal had become big news. As evening arrived, a large crowd had appeared outside the police station.

A TV reporter was talking straight to camera. 'Behind these walls lies the mystery all India is talking about. Did Jamal Malik, an uneducated eighteen-year-old boy from the slums of Mumbai, cheat or did he win fairly? And in the crowds all around me, there is an even bigger question: will he be back tonight to play for twenty million rupees?'

In a large house on the other side of the city, crime boss Javed was listening to these words on the news. He didn't recognise the photo of the boy who had pretended to be a new cook in his kitchen.

Several other people were in the dark room, lit only by the television screen – a few of Javed's men and their girlfriends. The only people there who recognised Jamal were Latika and Salim.

Javed changed the channel to one with pop music. He and one of the girls began dancing. He wanted to have a party, not watch a stupid television programme.

Latika took the chance to leave the room quietly. Salim followed and found her watching television in a different room. On one side of her face was a long scar to remind her of that day at the VT Station. A tear ran down it now as she listened to the news about Jamal.

'That guy,' said Salim from the door. 'He will never give up.' He smiled and shook his head. 'Never.'

To Latika, Salim was no more than one of Javed's men. And so it was a shock when he held something out to her – car keys.

'Go,' said Salim.

'But … '

'Just drive. There won't be another chance.'

Latika took the keys.

'He will kill you,' she said.

But Salim had made his decision. 'I'll take care of Javed.'

Latika looked at the open door. Fear ate at her heart. 'I can't.'

'You have to,' said Salim, putting his mobile phone into her hand. He brushed the hair away from her scar. 'And for what I've done, please forgive me.'

'Have a good life,' Salim said quietly as she ran out to the car.

* * *

The crowd outside the studio was huge – everybody wanted to see Jamal, to be a part of history. The cheers grew louder when the police van arrived with Jamal in the back. The people closest to the van reached out, wanting to get near to the millionaire *chai-wallah*.

'Good luck!'

'We love you, Jamal!'

He looked out at the blinding lights and the sea of people all around him. It was time to face his destiny.

* * *

All around the city, people crowded in front of televisions. At the call centre, the desks were empty. In the streets, crowds stood in front of television shop windows.

They all watched as the programme's music started and Prem Kumar led Jamal back out into the studio to the cheers of the crowd.

Prem smiled into the camera. 'Welcome back to *Who Wants To Be A Millionaire?*!' He turned to Jamal. 'I can safely say that tonight is the biggest night of both our lives. You can walk away with ten million rupees, or you can take the biggest chance in television history and go for the final question – and an amazing twenty million rupees! So ... are you ready for that question?'

'Yes.'

The air in the studio felt electric as the lights went down. Prem looked at the question on the card in his hands. 'Are you a big reader, Jamal?'

'I can read.' There was some nervous laughter from the audience.

When silence returned, Prem read out the final question:

In Alexander Dumas' book The Three Musketeers, two of the musketeers are called Athos and Porthos. What was the name of the third musketeer?

A: Aramis
B: Cardinal Richelieu
C: D'Artagnan
D: Planchet

Jamal couldn't help laughing. He remembered that day all those years ago when their teacher had called him and his brother 'the two musketeers'. He remembered telling Salim, when they first met Latika, that she could be the third musketeer to their Athos and Porthos! That's how he had viewed the three of them once – 'the three musketeers', always together.

'He's smiling,' Prem told the audience. 'I guess you know the answer, Jamal.'

Jamal continued to smile. 'Would you believe it? I don't.' He didn't seem to care.

'You don't know?' asked Prem. 'So you're going to take the ten million and walk?'

'No,' said Jamal. 'I'll play.'

The audience let out a shocked sound.

'Let me remind you,' said Prem. 'If you get the answer

wrong, you lose *everything* ...'

Jamal took a breath. 'I'd like to use my last lifeline and Phone-A-Friend.'

Now that Jamal had said these words, there was no turning back: he had to play.

The sound of a telephone came over the studio speakers as the computer put the call through.

'It's ringing,' said Prem. 'Who is it?'

'It's my brother's mobile phone.'

The phone continued to ring.

'Maybe he's gone for a walk,' said Jamal.

'Is he the kind of brother who'd go for a walk on a twenty-million rupee question?' smiled Prem.

Jamal shook his head uncertainly. 'It's the only number I know.'

* * *

Latika had driven as fast as she could to get into the city. For the first time in years, she felt sure about what she was doing – she wanted to be with Jamal, the only person she had ever loved. But the closer she came to the television studio, the worse the traffic became. Realising that she would never get there in time, she parked the car and ran out into the street. She joined a group of people outside the window of a television shop.

When she heard the final question, she too let out a surprised laugh. She watched as the computer called Jamal's Phone-A-Friend number. Like everyone else, she waited.

Suddenly she realised – Salim could not answer because he had given his mobile phone to her! But she had left it in the car! She turned and ran back to the parked car as quickly as she could. She only hoped that she wasn't too late.

✶ ✶ ✶

In the studio, Prem was shaking his head. 'Nobody is answering. You're alone, Jamal.' Behind the cameras, one of the programme's producers was getting ready to end the call.

But then suddenly a woman's voice answered the phone. 'Jamal?'

'I'm guessing,' said Prem, '*that* isn't your brother. Who is this?'

'My name is Latika.'

Jamal had to stop himself from jumping up, laughing, dancing. Latika! He didn't know how she had got Salim's phone or why she was answering. He didn't care!

'Well, Latika, let's be clear,' said Prem. 'Jamal is going to read you the final question again. You have twenty seconds … .'

✶ ✶ ✶

When he heard Latika's name on TV, Javed called for
silence. Anger rose inside him.

'Latika!' he shouted, knowing that there would be no
answer. His thoughts raced. Where had she gone?

'Salim!' he shouted.

There was no answer. Salim had locked himself in
the bathroom. Here he took a bag of Javed's money and
emptied it into the bath. He looked down at all the money
and thought of all the pain that had been its price. He
knew that he had been a part of it.

It was too late to save himself, but he could still save
Jamal and Latika. He took out his gun and waited.

∗ ∗ ∗

'Latika, is that really you?' asked Jamal.

'Yes,' she said, happily

'The question, Jamal, the question!' said Prem urgently.

Jamal quickly read out the question to Latika.

'Fifteen seconds left!' said Prem.

'Where are you?' Jamal asked.

'I'm safe,' replied Latika.

'Ten seconds! Latika, what do you think?'

There was a pause and then Latika said, 'I don't know.
I've never known.' She gave a surprised laugh, full of
shared memories. Jamal thought back to the night that he
had first met Latika, when they were seven years old. He
remembered how he had persuaded Salim to let her be the
third musketeer. So much had happened since then, but
he had never stopped thinking about her.

And then the twenty seconds were over. Latika's voice
was cut off.

'Jamal, you really are on your own,' said Prem. 'Your final answer, for twenty million rupees?' Jamal did not know the answer and there was nobody to help him. But he did not look worried as he said, 'My answer is A.'

'Because?'

Jamal smiled. 'Just ... *because*.' He had no other explanation to offer.

Prem asked the computer to show the final answer. He looked down at the screen for a long time. Everybody in the studio held their breath; it seemed that the whole world was holding its breath.

'Jamal Malik,' said Prem, 'call-centre *chai-wallah* from Mumbai ... for twenty million rupees ... you answered A. I have to tell you that is ... ' He paused. The seconds felt like years, and then, '... THE RIGHT ANSWER!'

The crowd were up on their feet, cheering and cheering. Jamal had won! He'd won more money than anybody in television history! But Jamal wasn't thinking about the money – he was thinking about the voice on the phone.

* * *

Javed was banging on the bathroom door.

'Salim! Open this door! Salim!'

His men behind him had their guns ready. One of them ran at the door with his shoulder. As soon as it was open, they ran inside.

Salim was waiting with a sad smile on his face. He was sitting in a bath full of bank notes. He began to shoot at the men, and Javed was the first to fall.

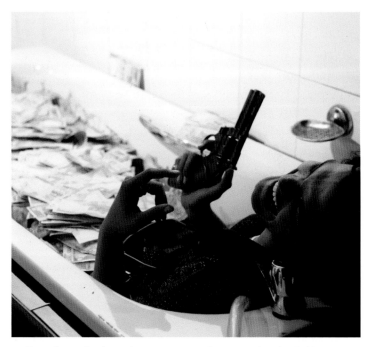

But then the boss's men were shooting back. Salim was hit again and again. His head fell back onto the money.

With his last breath, he whispered, 'God is great.'

＊ ＊ ＊

Mumbai's VT Station was quiet at this time of night. Jamal sat alone, hardly able to believe what had happened. The end of the show had been like a dream – the cheers of the crowd, Prem's hand on his shoulder, the huge cheque for twenty million rupees. Twenty million rupees! He had more money now than he had ever imagined.

But money was not what Jamal was looking for. He only wanted one thing, and he had spent most of his life chasing it. He wanted to be with Latika. As soon as the show was over, he had come here, to the old meeting place.

He looked up now and could hardly believe his eyes. She was here, on the platform opposite, where she stood, looking around uncertainly.

Jamal knew that he could never let her go again. Latika saw him as he began to cross the platforms. And then they were together at last.

'I thought we'd meet again only in death,' said Latika.

'I knew you'd watch the programme,' said Jamal.

He reached out to touch her face. She could not look at him when he saw the long scar on her cheek. But Jamal just kissed the scar gently. He felt that all his life had been leading up to this one perfect moment.

'This is our destiny,' he said.

EPILOGUE

In the biggest quiz programme on Indian television,
Jamal Malik has won twenty million rupees.
How did he do it?

A:

B:

C:

D: It is his destiny.

MAKING SLUMDOG

'And the Oscar goes to ... *Slumdog Millionaire*!' In 2009, *Slumdog Millionaire* won a total of eight Oscars, including awards for best film, best director and best music. It's an exciting, fast-moving love story, set in the Indian city of Mumbai. It was very popular around the world and it brought attention to the lives of India's street children.

From book to film

Slumdog Millionaire came from a book called *Q & A* by an Indian writer, Vikas Swarup. Swarup took the idea for his book from real life – a young boy from the slums of Mumbai won the popular quiz show *Who Wants To Be A Millionaire?*. Simon Beaufoy (writer of hit film *The Full Monty*) adapted *Q & A* into a film.

Some of the cast at the Oscar Awards

Casting

'Casting was very difficult and it took a long time,' said director, Danny Boyle. "The film shows Jamal, Salim and Latika at three different times in their lives – when they're seven, thirteen and eighteen years old. So we had to find three actors for each character.'

Director, Danny Boyle

Most of the cast for the film came from India. The film makers put up advertisements all over Mumbai looking for children to star in the film. They didn't have to be actors. Some of the children in the film came from the slums, including the children who play young Salim and young Latika.

Dev Patel, who plays the older Jamal, was one of the few actors from the UK. He had done some TV work, but *Slumdog* was his first film.

Anil Kapoor (Prem Kumar) is a big star in India. 'I didn't read the script,' he laughed, 'but I knew immediately I wanted to be in this film.'

MILLIONAIRE

English or Hindi?

At first, the film was all in English. Then the film makers decided to have some Hindi in the film to make it more real. Hindi and English are both spoken in India, but it is unlikely that street children would speak much English.

Filming

Most of *Slumdog Millionaire* was filmed on the busy streets of Mumbai. This came with some of its own problems.

'Mumbai is always changing,' said Danny Boyle. 'You choose somewhere to film, then when you arrive the next day, you find that a wall has been built in the night! You just have to accept it and carry on filming.'

Films and film stars are hugely popular in India. Hundreds of people would stop to watch the filming, and they would stay all day!

The *Slumdog* team also filmed a lot in the slums. 'We wanted to show people the real India,' said Simon Beaufoy. 'People are poor but the slums are lively places, with lots of friendship and laughter.'

'In India, film makers are called dream sellers,' smiles Danny Boyle. 'I like that idea!'

> **If you could make a film about a city, where would you choose? Why?**

Find out more at: www.slumdogmillionairemovie.co.uk

What do these words mean? You can use a dictionary.
award   cast / casting   script

India

India is a country of huge differences. It has a fast-growing economy but 24% of its people live on less than one US dollar a day*. To understand India means understanding the importance of religion in the country, along with its troubled history.

* Source: World Bank report, 2005

Hinduism

Hinduism is India's main religion. Approximately 82% of the country is Hindu. There are over 330 million Hindu gods. Hindus choose the gods they want to follow, and worship them at temples.

A Hindu festival, Mumbai

Reincarnation and the caste system

Hindus believe in reincarnation – when you die, you are born again, and if you live a good life, your next life will be better. Hindus believe that they are born into one of four groups ('castes'). The lowest caste were often treated very badly by people in higher castes. Today, laws are in place to give equal rights to those in lower castes, but the caste system still exists, especially outside the cities.

British India

In the 1600s, England started trading with India. The East India Trading Company established trading stations all over India. They mainly traded in tea and cotton. By the early 1800s, India was completely under British rule.

Picking tea in India, 1880

Gandhi and independence

By the start of the 20th century, many Indians wanted independence from Britain. A man called Gandhi played an important part in India's fight for independence. Gandhi believed that people of all religions and castes were equal and he wanted to achieve an independent India, through peaceful protest.

But Gandhi couldn't get independence peacefully. An independent India meant a Hindu India and many Muslims wanted their own Muslim state. In 1947, the decision was made to divide the country into two parts – one for Muslims (the new country of Pakistan) and one for Hindus. Gandhi knew this would be terrible for India and he was right. It was no longer safe for Muslims and Hindus to live in the same areas. Hundreds of thousands of people were killed as they tried to escape from their homes.

Some Hindus did not agree with Gandhi because he believed in helping all religions, including Muslims. In 1948, Gandhi was shot dead by a Hindu.

Today, India is a free country, but there are still many problems between the Hindus and the Muslims.

Mahatma Gandhi, 1946

**Find out more at: www.mkgandhi.org
www.bbc.co.uk/religion/religions/hinduism**

Is there anything similar about India and your own country?

What do these words mean? You can use a dictionary.

economy   temple   trade / trading   independence / independent
protest   divide   worship

STREET CHILDREN

India is home to more than eleven million street children. Some of these children have no parents to look after them, like Jamal and Salim in *Slumdog Millionaire*. Others have run away from home, or have been abandoned by their families who couldn't afford to feed them. Some live with their families on the streets and have to work to get money.

Life for India's street children is difficult and dangerous. Rukshana, a fifteen-year-old living on the streets of Mumbai, speaks about her life.

"I come from a village in Bengal. When my father died, my uncle threw me and my sister and mother out of the house. We came to Mumbai to work. I was nine and my sister Deepa was five. We never had enough to eat, and my mother became ill. I started begging on the streets but my mother didn't like that. So I worked on the trains, selling jewellery and other things. My mother died two years ago. Now, Deepa and I are on our own.

I sleep outside with Deepa and five other girls, near one of the train stations in Mumbai. It's too dangerous to sleep alone. When we wake up, we hide our sheets in a tree. Then we go to the station toilets to wash.

We work on the trains all day until 9 pm usually. If the police catch us, we have to pay them money. I usually earn 100 - 200 rupees (four dollars) a day.

We go to see films about three times a week. I like films with Mithun – he's an

A boy selling food at a railway station, New Delhi

actor from Bengal.

I really want to learn to read and write, and then get married. I want my sister to go to school. I want to live in my own house and have my own gold jewellery. Those are my plans for the future."

[Interview with Rukshana adapted from the *New Internationalist* magazine]

Find out more at: www.magicbusindia. org and www.childlineindia.org

IN INDIA

Organised gangs

Some children are part of gangs, run by adults. The children are sent out to beg or sing traditional Indian songs for money. Sometimes they have to steal or sell drugs. They have to give any money that they receive to the gang leaders. Some children have to have completely healthy arms or legs amputated — this way the children receive more money when they beg.

Help for street children

There are several charities in India which help street children. They provide street schools where children can learn to read or write, or places where children can spend the night in safety. All of them try to protect children from the dangers of the street.

What are the most important things that charities can do to improve life for street children, do you think?

A slum school in North Goa

What do these words mean? You can use a dictionary.
abandon   gang   drug   amputate   charity

PROLOGUE–CHAPTER 1

Before you read

Use your dictionary for these questions.

1 Complete the sentences with these words. You can use a dictionary.

**beg cheat cheer contestant cricket
emblem presenter quiz slums studio**

   a) The crowd began to … when their team won the game.
   b) I like most sports, but I don't really understand … .
   c) The government wants to pull down all of the … in the city and build better places to live.
   d) She can usually answer all of the questions on TV … shows.
   e) Many homeless people in the city … for money in the streets.
   f) The national … of India has got three lions on it.
   g) The programme's … asks all of the questions.
   h) He tried to … in the exam by writing answers on his arm.
   i) They make the programme in front of a live audience at the TV … .
   j) Only one … can win the big prize in the new game show on TV.

2 Look at 'People and Places' on pages 4–5 and answer the questions.
   a) Who uses children to get money for himself?
   b) What city does Jamal come from?
   c) Who is younger, Jamal or Salim?
   d) Who does Jamal love?
   e) Why is Javed rich?
   f) Where does Jamal work?
   g) On which television programme is Jamal a contestant?

After you read

3 Answer the questions.
   a) At the start of the book, how much money has Jamal won already?
   b) How does the Inspector think Jamal won this money?
   c) Who is the presenter of *Who Wants To Be A Millionaire?*.
   d) What job does Jamal do at the call centre?

e) What book is the boys' teacher talking about?

f) What does the young Jamal want Amitabh Bachchan to do?

g) Why is the audience surprised that Jamal uses a 'lifeline' for the second question?

4 What do you think?

The Inspector does not believe that Jamal could know the answers. 'He's from the slums. What can a slumdog know?' Why do you think the inspector has this opinion?

5 **Writing**

Imagine you are Jamal as a young boy. Write in your diary about seeing Amitabh Bachchan. Include your feelings when Salim sold the picture of Amitabh.

CHAPTERS 2–3

Before you read

6 Complete the sentences with these words. You can use a dictionary.

bow   cloth   dump   orphanage   shock

a) He grew up in an ... after his parents died.

b) A ... is a kind of weapon.

c) All of the city's rubbish is put in one huge ... .

d) I had a terrible ... when I heard the bad news.

e) I usually clean the windows with a wet ... .

7 What do you think?

At the end of chapter 1, the studio audience does not think that Jamal will do very well in the quiz. Do you agree? Why or why not?

After you read

8 Find and correct the mistakes in these sentences.

a) Jamal is a Hindu.

b) Jamal's mother runs away.

c) The boys see a man dressed as the god Rama.

d) A group of policemen agree to help the boys.

e) Salim asks Latika to join them.

f) The children return to Juhu.

g) After Jamal answers the third question correctly, Prem Kumar wishes him good luck.

h) The yellow van at the city dump is from the police.

9 Complete these sentences with the correct names.

Arvind   Jamal   Latika   Maman   Punnoose   Salim

a) … is a terrible singer.

b) … wants to hear the children sing.

c) … holds a cloth over Arvind's mouth.

d) … thinks that he will be rich when he is a professional singer.

e) … is blinded.

f) … tries to get on the train but fails.

10 **Writing**

Write a letter to a newspaper asking for something to be done to save homeless children from people like Maman and his gang.

CHAPTERS 4–5

Before you read

11 Match the words with the definitions.

cubicle   exception   funeral   invent   revolver   scar

a) the ceremony held when someone dies

b) a gun

c) a change to the rules

d) to create something new, e.g. a new machine

e) the mark left on the skin by a deep cut

f) a small, closed, private area

12 Look at the photo on page 34. How much time has passed, do you think? How might the two brothers be earning a living now?

After you read

13 Put these events in the right order.

a) The brothers return to Mumbai.

b) Salim goes to meet a crime boss.

c) They arrive at the Taj Mahal.

d) Jamal learns where Latika is.

e) Salim points the gun at his own brother.

f) Jamal meets Arvind again.

g) Salim shoots and kills Maman.

h) An opera is performed at the Taj Mahal.

i) Jamal is given some American money.

j) The three children find an empty hotel.

k) The brothers travel all over the country by train.

14 What do you think?
Was Salim right to shoot Maman? Why or why not?

15 Writing
Imagine you are a newspaper reporter. Write an account of the events on Pila Street on the night Maman died.

CHAPTERS 6–7

Before you read

16 In what jobs do people need to use **head-sets**?

17 Which sentence can be completed with *insisted*?
    a) 'Excuse me,' he … . 'Where's the station?'
    b) 'You must come to dinner tomorrow,' she … . 'I won't take no for an answer!'
    c) 'Have a good day!' he … .

18 How long do you think it will be before Jamal sees Salim and Latika again? What do you think he will say to both of them?

After you read

19 Who says these things? Write the correct name.
    Jamal   Latika   Prem Kumar   Salim
    a) 'Is that you, brother?'
    b) 'I will *never* forgive you!'
    c) 'Go, before he kills us both!'
    d) 'Just trust me.'

20 Answer the questions.
   a) Who does Salim work for now?
   b) How does Jamal get into Javed's house?
   c) Where does Jamal say he will wait every day for Latika?
   d) Why does one of Salim's men cut Latika's face?
   e) How does Prem try to give Jamal an answer?

21 What do you think?
   In your opinion, why does Prem Kumar give Jamal the wrong answer?

CHAPTER 8—EPILOGUE

Before you read

22 Do you usually prefer to pay for things by *cheque*, cash or credit card? Why?

23 What do you think will happen to Latika? And Salim?

After you read

24 Are these sentences true or false? Correct the false sentences.
   a) Jamal goes home right after the programme ends.
   b) At first the police inspector does not trust Jamal.
   c) Jamal tells the Inspector how he knew all the answers.
   d) Javed wants to watch *Who Wants To Be A Millionaire?*.
   e) The final question is about a book.
   f) Latika gives Jamal the correct answer.
   g) Salim is killed by Javed's men.
   h) Jamal and Latika finally meet again at the TV studio.

25 Writing
   Write about Jamal and Latika's life, a year after they found each other at the station. What did they do next? What did they do with the money? Where did they live? Did they stay together?

26 What do you think?
   Do you believe in 'destiny'? Why or why not?